LIVING DESERT

WALT DISNEY'S

LIVING DESERT

A TRUE-LIFE ADVENTURE

by Jane Werner
and the Staff of the Walt Disney Studio

BASED ON THE FILM NARRATION BY
James Algar · Winston Hibler · Ted Sears

SIMON AND SCHUSTER · NEW YORK

THE NEXT TITLE IN THIS SERIES:

Vanishing Prairie

FOREWORD

IT IS NOW more than five years since the release of our first True-Life Adventure film, "SEAL ISLAND." We did not know what the public response would be to a film in which animals in their wild state were the only actors, in which Nature itself was the dramatist, while we merely stood by as cameramen and editors of the story.

FOREWORD

The response was overwhelming. The True-Life Adventures have found a place in the lives and hearts of so many people that we have been encouraged to continue developing the series, through six other half-hour films to this first full-length feature.

The invaluable cooperation of eminent naturalists and skilled and sensitive nature photographers has brought to us on film records of some of the activities of Nature's wild creatures which have seldom, if ever, been photographed before. But any motion picture, because of its nature, provides only a fleeting impression. We felt the need to provide a more permanent record, if possible, and so began to plan the transposing of these films into book form.

This book is the first of a series of True-Life Adventure books. Its photographs, taken especially for this project, in many cases by the same men who worked on the motion picture, parallel the action of the film. Its text amplifies the story so briefly told in the film's narration. We hope that it will bring to readers, in permanent form, some of the same pleasures to be found in viewing the film and that it will do its part in reawakening the interest of many thousands of people in Nature's wild creatures with whom we share this planet.

Walt Disney

Contents

Walt Disney Productions staff members
and associates who supplied color
photographs on the pages listed, include:

Yale Gracey, 101, 104; Stuart Jewell, 33, 108, 110 (right);
Paul Kenworthy, 39, 46, 47, 49-53, 55, 63-68, 70, 72, 73, 75-77,
79-83, 86, 88-93, 97, 99; Fred Kopietz, 22, 42-43, 62;
Tad Nichols, 105; Art Riley, 21 (top), 23, 26, 45, 84, 102-103,
106, 107, 109, 111 (bottom).

Assistance of the following,
who supplied the color photographs on the pages
listed, is also gratefully acknowledged:

Camera Clix, 19; Robert Crandall, 39, 97, 99;
Harry Crockett, 28, 29; Joseph Muench, 13-14, 21 (bottom), 56-57;
R. C. and Claire Meyer Proctor, 24-25, 110 (left), 111 (top).

The drawings throughout the book are
by Campbell Grant with the exception of
the maps on pages 15 and 17, done by
the staff of Walt Disney Productions

THE LIVING DESERT

How It All Began

LOOKING OUT over a desert with its naked hills, its vast stretching wastes of lifeless rock and sand, with its weirdly fashioned patterns of stone and plant, twisted and stunted beneath the glare of sun, we cannot help wondering how all this came to be.

Did the life-giving gift of sunlight turn here to a curse, like King Midas's Golden Touch?

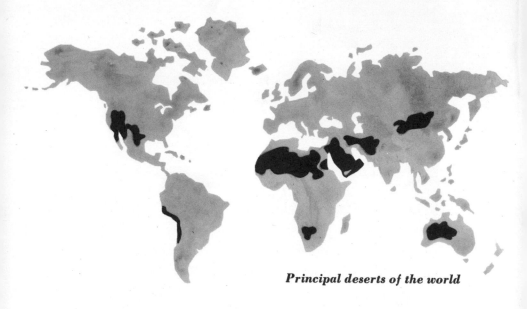

Principal deserts of the world

Only in part. It is the winds, even more than the sun, which have made the desert, and which keep on remolding it even today. And behind the winds, the mountains.

Across the face of our globe, prevailing winds blow almost constantly, bringing clouds to the land areas, and life-giving rain.

Since the oceans of the world cover more than two-thirds of its surface, and since moisture is constantly being drawn up from the oceans' surface into the wind-driven clouds above, it would seem that all parts of the land should receive moisture enough.

This might perhaps be true, were it not for the mountains. There are a number of places on the earth where mountain chains keep the moisture-laden winds from reaching great stretches of land beyond. These thirsty stretches are the great deserts of the world—the Sahara

and the Kalahari in Africa, the broad Near-Eastern waste-
lands of Arabia and Iran, Asia's ancient Gobi, the vast
barren heart of Western Australia, Atacama in South
America, and in North America the Great American
Desert.

Near the western edge of North America, the Sierra
Nevada and Cascade ranges rise squarely across the
path of the winds from the Pacific. Like an enormous
granite wall a thousand miles long, they keep the rain-
bearing westerlies from reaching a major portion of the
continent.

West of the mountains, where the clouds drop their
moisture, fertile valleys stretch. East of the mountains
all is barren desolation. Here the desert begins.

This desert created in part by the granite blockade
of the Sierras, the Great American Desert, is one of the
largest in the world.

The Great American Desert

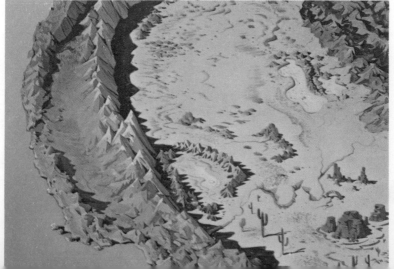

The highest point in the United States is found in the range looming above it—jagged, snow-streaked Mt. Whitney, towering nearly fifteen thousand feet above sea level. But in the very shadow of this majestic peak is Death Valley, bitterest of all deserts, and the lowest point on the American continent.

From Death Valley east to the plains of Texas this desert stretches, and from a corner of Oregon deep into Old Mexico.

These sunbaked hills and silent dunes seem to have been here since time began. Yet they are forever changing, for in nature nothing is so constant as change.

Once all this valley lay beneath a vast and nameless sea. But Nature, through an age of violent, volcanic moods, pulled towering mountain ranges into the Pacific on the one hand, while with the other she was thrusting up the sea bottom, coated with its slow layers of limestone deposits, into the sun.

As the ancient waves receded, they left exposed an ocean's skeleton. Here, where lost pools were trapped to be sucked up drop by drop beneath the sun, lie gleaming beds of salt deposits that extend for miles. Here fossils of long-vanished sea creatures were pressed between layers of rock which once was mud, the form at least of their fluted shells quite perfectly preserved. Here trunks of still more ancient forest trees, buried, then transformed underground into minerals rich and strange, and finally uncovered, lie endlessly under the sky.

Mt. Whitney in the High Sierras   *Bad Water in Death Valley*

Ravaged day-long by the blaze of sun, swept by dry, roving winds by night, the raw new land waited, crisping and crumbling, as ages drifted by.

Barred by the mountains from gentle rains which might have softened the surface rock into fertile soil, the land lay prey to the sun and wind, to Nature's most violent moods.

As the temperature veered swiftly and wildly from the sizzle of noonday to the chill of night, the dry rocks quivered and cracked. Then teasing winds fingered their way into the crevices and began their work of erosion.

As the softer rocks crumbled beneath the wind's pressure, sand particles from them went swirling through the air. Against other rocks they rasped like countless files; and the action of abrasion rubbed and polished rock masses into weird and fantastically beautiful forms.

Sometimes the winds stirred up miniature tornadoes— "dust devils" like those that even today dance along the parched basins, catching up sand and shriveled debris and carrying them a thousand feet into the sky.

Sometimes these tiny sandstorms built up into howling blizzards, blasting the living bark from stunted shrubs, snatching the soil away from groping roots, burying trees as the huge dunes shifted, carving the very rock itself. And so they do today.

Water too was at work in forming the desert. Now and again, as if by freak chance, dark thunderheads found their way over the mountain barrier. With the

Eroded hills (above) and shifting dunes

Desert rains, through thousands of years,
have cut many rock-walled canyons.

extravagance characteristic of the desert, the clouds flung down their burdens of rain in cloudbursts wild and swift.

Without surface soil to absorb the moisture, or networks of roots to hold it back, these desert rains went rushing forward in riotous streams. They slashed deep river beds through sheer rock. They gouged the fantastic canyons and gorges we marvel at today. They scarred the desert with steep-sided arroyos. Then they dwindled and disappeared.

Today the desert is a land seared by sun, parched by the wind, scoured by sandstorms which blast everything in their path. It has seas of burning sand, where temperatures reach furnace-like heat. It lures the traveler with views of shimmering lakes which treacherously fade before his eyes. In truth they are no more than the optical illusion known as a mirage. Bending of light rays as they pass through air layers of differing densities causes the shimmering effect. It may also cause the light rays to seem to be coming from a direction other than the true one; thus images of distant objects such as lakes and trees may appear in the sky, often inverted. Many a thirsty traveler sees such sights, promising refreshment and cool shade, whereas in reality all that waits ahead is sand and wind and sun.

How anything can live in this harsh region is a mystery to most of us. To us, the desert seems a place unsuited for life—a region of dead seas, dead mountains, and dead landscapes. Yet strangely, though to our careless glance the desert appears dead, Nature has created there a whole world of living things.

To Nature, this is a region teeming with life, as vital a part of her scheme of things as the lushest tropical setting. So this is the story of
Nature's Living Desert.

In the desert
Nature has twisted
many of her
forms of life.
Here are plants
without leaves,
animals which
drink no water,
skies which rarely
offer the blessing
of rain.
Still the desert
throbs with life
and its own color,
as in these
bright blossoms
of the barrel cacti.

THE STRUGGLE FOR SURVIVAL

How the Plants Adapt

THE DESERT is the stage for a tense drama—the drama of the struggle for survival. Its characters are many—every desert insect, animal and plant. For life is not easy here. The desert sets its terms, and those who wish to live there must adapt themselves to its demands.

Desert plants cannot afford the luxury of a lavish

display of broad green leaves. Most plants breathe in air and receive sunlight through their leaves, and in leaf factories convert their raw materials into usable plant food. But moisture evaporates from leaf surfaces, too, and desert plants have no moisture to spare.

Sunlight they have in plenty, and what they need they absorb largely through their stems. But moisture they must conserve with care. So they sacrifice wasteful leaf surfaces; they roll leaves into tubes with little surface, or shrivel them into needles, or thicken them into spine-covered spongy reservoirs.

A few trees, whose fibers still remember life in other areas, put out small, thin, green leaves after the scant desert rains; but these drop as soon as the drought returns.

Instead most desert plants have developed thick stems, in which they store water supplies. These water-filled tissues have given to their whole group of plants the name of succulents, or juicy ones.

In some the stem is swollen round as a barrel; the largest of these—sometimes a gigantic ten feet tall after 100 years of growth—are called barrel cacti. The roly-poly little ones, from one to twelve inches around, are called hedgehogs, for their bristling tufts of spines. The cactus family seems to delight in odd shapes, as in the organ cactus with its row of towering "pipes" and the countless prickly, spined and twisted oddities.

Water-bottle stems might have proved to be the downfall of the cactus family; for on a thirsty desert any juicy plant is tempting food for animals. But the cactus has taken that into account. Instead of leaves it has developed slender thorny spines, some barbed and some several inches long and needle-sharp. Many animals will not risk a mouthful of barbed needles, even for a drink of water. So each cactus has built-in self-protection against being eaten up.

Only the birds seem to have come to terms with the cacti. Trees are scarce in the desert, they find at nesting time. Beside the rare desert watering holes, where some underground river springs briefly to the surface, a slender desert willow may bend (not a true willow, but a small, slender tree, a relative of the catalpa, flowering in delicate

Thrasher at nest   *Flycatcher on cactus*

pink). Or there may be a smoke tree (of the pea family) beckoning with its feathery top; or a swaying, restless-leaved cottonwood, reminding bird travelers of greener, distant countrysides.

There are shrubs—creosote bushes and spicy-smelling gray-green sage; juniper and the pale-leaved desert holly. But there are few homesites for nest-minded birds, so they nest in the unfriendly-looking cactus.

Its seeming drawbacks they turn to advantage. They break off the thorns where they will build their nests. The rest they value for the protection they give. Home in a cactus is a fortress well guarded from below by a thousand bayonets.

Each bird, it seems, has a favorite brand of cactus.

Nest of house finch

The thrashers prefer the tree-like cholla, which may grow ten feet tall; in its thorny joints they build their nests and raise their young. The flat, brown-bristled mat of the prickly pear cactus invites the peaceful dove to make her home among its spoon-shaped joints.

The cactus wren also raises her young within these prickly walls. In fact, she goes the others one better; she builds not one but several nests. Which one she occupies remains her secret. So when a prowling snake, such as the red racer, comes calling, he often finds an empty apartment awaiting him.

The fluted columns of the "desert sky-scraper," the giant saguaro which may tower 30 to 50 feet, house the restless, swift red-tailed hawk and the little elf owl. In its straight trunk columns, often three feet around, the woodpecker, too, pecks out his hole and settles down, high above the sun-baked rock, comfortably at home.

Elf owl in saguaro

The Desert Tortoise

There are desert animals, as well as plants, which store up supplies of water for the long dry spells. Chief among these is the desert tortoise. In fact, he does not need to live near a water supply, for he has a way of storing his own.

He feeds on the green foliage of succulent plants and then converts this juicy fodder into water inside his body. And for the long periods when there is no green food to be had, he stores up the clear watery fluid in two sacs beneath his shell.

The desert tortoise is not a big fellow; from stem to stern his high-domed upper shell does not usually measure much more than nine inches. But he has a ponderous dignity all his own. Perhaps it is partly his stately walk, for he plants his club-shaped back feet flat in the manner of an elephant. Perhaps it is the nodding motion of his head, as he moves about solemnly munching berries and leaves.

He thrives on the heat of the desert day. In the morning, when he waddles out of his burrow, he is sluggish and does not care to move far. But as the day warms, the sun's heat seems to rouse him, drumming down upon his shell. Now his step quickens, his manner brightens, his roving eye is more alert.

There is a limit, though, to the sun even he can take; and the desert day often passes that limit. When heat waves shimmer glassily over the sand, and the arms of the Joshua trees seem to droop under their burden of sun, our tortoise retreats to his burrow or to the scant shade of dull brown grasses just the tone of his own brown coat.

No one can spend a lifetime dozing in the shade, though. As the courting season comes on, a restlessness drives our tortoise out on a shambling, yet determined, search for a mate.

Plod, plod, he moves carefully along, stepping on the claws alone of his front feet, but planting the rear feet solidly. He pauses here and there to munch a tasty leaf, but his eye is out for a likely female. She seems more important now than food.

At last he spots one, behind a cactus, and he makes his way to her. Scarcely has he greeted her, with stately nods, when a rival comes along.

Rivalry, as always, means a battle. Our tortoise knows

the battle rules. He lowers his head to feel the firm, reassuring curve of the skid projecting forward from his lower shell. If he can hook this under the other male's shell and flip him over on his back, he will win.

Of course, the other male has a skid too. Our tortoise eyes this weapon soberly and matches his foot-work to the other's speed, so that they stay face to face. Step by wary circling step they both move forward until at last they meet. With a dull clash of shell on shell they push against each other, straining with their strong back legs. Up go their foreshells, while each rival struggles with skids and forepaws to tip the other over.

For the moment our tortoise has the advantage—not that the bored lady seems to care which one wins. One well-placed thrust and he will be the victor—but a small stone slips under one of his back feet. He staggers, and

A triangle among tortoises

Skids and forepaws are tortoise weapons.

Over on his back he goes.

If he cannot right himself, he will die.

his rival is quick to advance. Back, back he pushes him until a hedgehog cactus blocks his retreat. Its spines cannot prick him through his shell's armor, but it throws him off balance—and over on his back he goes.

Now his legs thrash wildly, and his little eyes roll— with good reason, for he can scarcely breathe. The whole weight of his internal organs is pressing on his lungs. If he cannot right himself he will die.

The first panic passes; wild thrashing, he senses, will never help him now. Painfully gathering his strength, he rolls his weight from side to side. Back and forth rocks the dome-shaped shell. Still he cannot right himself.

At last one groping toe finds what it sought—a crack in the dry earth. But the toe slips out; the shell rocks back.

Now at least the tortoise has a goal. Back and forth— back and forth—and on the next roll he gains a toehold. Then with burning lungs he forces himself to one last effort—and over he goes, back on all fours once more.

For a moment he stands weakly blinking in the sun, his gasping mouth gulping in fresh air. He is close to sunstroke, weakened by the struggle. The female for whom he battled is out of sight; the victor has led her away. But our tortoise does not mind; he is glad to be alive. He will not father a family perhaps, at least not this season. But for the moment he is glad to rest, so into the shade of a cholla hedge he crawls and settles himself for a nap.

A nine-banded armadillo

All's Fair

Every suit of armor has its weak spot, it seems. Look at the armadillo. Sometimes called "the pig in a suit of mail," the armadillo's scaly covering has helped him to survive from prehistoric times.

In prehistoric times, one of his ancestors used to be the size of a small rhinoceros. The armadillo we find today on the desert's fringes, perhaps sitting up on his hind legs, braced with his tail, searching a cactus patch for insects with dim-sighted eyes, is not more than two and a half feet long.

His weaknesses are poor vision, hearing too weak to warn him of danger, and big, unarmored ears. Flat bony plates or scales protect him from the tip of his nose to the end of his tail—all but the ears!

Now the coyote, the smiling, doglike desert hunter, considers armadillo meat delicious. And he knows about those unprotected ears. Sometimes he is fortunate enough to come upon an armadillo far from its grass-lined tunnel home. There is the armadillo, perhaps with a group of friends, padding along, snout to the ground, grunting softly to itself as it hunts for bugs.

Dinosaurs belong to the past

Up steals the coyote—dangerously close before the armadillo sniffs the danger. Away goes the armadillo, at an amazing speed. In a cactus thicket, or the shelter of a thorny chaparral, he starts to dig. As soon as he is below the surface, he braces himself against the tunnel walls—and no hunter could possibly drag him out.

After sniffing and waiting around a while, the coyote will give up the hunt at last, and howl his disappointment to the sky.

The chuckwalla has a similar method of saving his timid skin. Oh, he looks brave and fierce enough; he is a large lizard built like a miniature dinosaur. He is splendidly designed for desert life, with a sand-colored coat to hide him from enemies and a harsh skin that slows loss of moisture from his body. But he will run at the first sign of a threat, run for the nearest crevice and dive into it. There he inflates his belly until he is tightly

. . . but chuckwallas are built on the same pattern.

wedged into the space. Rather like the armadillo in his burrow, he is safe because it is almost impossible for an enemy to drag him out.

Survival on the desert is a daily test of ingenuity. Some creatures rely on speed, some use deception, like the sand lizard, a speedy fellow too, but with a salt-and-pepper coat which makes him almost invisible against the sand. For further safety, he buries himself in the sand dunes, with only an eye exposed to observe the world around him.

He likes to doze on a sunny rock, soaking in the warmth he needs to make his little system tick well; but there he may be visible to enemies—the black and yellow king snake for one. If his camouflage fails, and the king snake strikes, the lizard too must fall back on speed. One quick dart and the sunny rock is bare when the king snake's fangs come down.

The defense may be sharp teeth or raking claws, it may be a strong scent which drives away hunters, or a pair of poison-filled fangs. Desert creatures equipped with all these we shall meet; but for every defense, there is an offensive plan to match it. For Nature plays no favorites, and life in her kingdom is always a matter of give and take.

Desert lizard

Give and Take

The Omnivorous Coati

THE DRY river wash makes a sheltered sandy highway
for a migrating family of coati mundis. All a watcher
from the bank above could see, much of the time, would
be a row of black-ringed upstanding tails waving in the
air. The coati stands only ten inches high at the shoulder,
but his tail is two feet long—as long as his body from
nose to rump—and he carries it proudly aloft.

The coatis are on the prowl for food, and chances are

they will find it, for almost anything they come upon is food to a coati—insects, lizards, rodents, fruits, or eggs. He will even eat poisonous scorpions for snacks, being more or less immune to their poison. And a prickly pear cactus fruit is a treat.

These lively animals were originally from South America. But they are tropical cousins of the American raccoon. You can see their resemblance in the way they use their forepaws like little hands, in their sharp masked face, even in their ringed tails.

Like American raccoons, too, they are at home in the treetops. One reason their desert travels center about the dry washes is that the desert's few trees grow there.

Their nests are made in hollow logs if possible; they also like trees for climbing and hunting. No bird's nest with eggs is safe from these tree-climbing bands—not even the vulture's.

Here comes a mother coati with her young. (The father is almost twice the size of the mother but does not travel with her and the young.) She is training her children in the art of egg-hunting. They have been out half the night; perhaps they can find a last tasty morsel to take back to their nest and enjoy there before their midday nap.

Into the branches of the tree they leap, balancing with their tails. The children are ready for a game, and start to leap from branch to branch. But mother calls them back; she has seen an unguarded nest and sends

Egg-hunting is an art among coatis.

the children toward it, while she pursues a lizard she has spotted, sunning himself below.

Two of the young coatis snatch up eggs and run off with them in their forepaws. Back at the nest in the cottonwood log they settle down for a meal; but the eggs are so big they cannot sink their sharp little canine teeth into the shells. They roll the eggs against roots and stones, but not until mother arrives do they get the eggs opened, and then mother, out of sorts because the lizard got away, leaving only his replaceable tail in her grasp, takes more than her share. Still there is enough to go around, and soon, curled up in a furry ball, the family is asleep.

In Monument Valley
desert scenery
reaches a peak
of haunting beauty.
There wind,
along with water,
through countless ages,
has scraped
and polished
spires and monoliths
and towering walls
of richly colored rock
into mute monuments
to an unknown
eternal power.

The peccary, American
cousin of the wild boar

The Peppery Peccary

Far up the draw, where the last muddy dampness lingers around the roots of a clump of desert willows, a conversation of soft grunts and barks hums on the clear desert air.

A band of peccaries have found the bit of moisture and are giving their young the rare desert treat of a good mud wallow. Their rough fur coats of salt and pepper hue were not planned for desert sun; so whenever they can, they stay close to shade and water.

It is easy to tell where the peccaries have been, for they leave behind a strong musky scent difficult to mistake. In this group are several males and four females, each with her twin young—one pair only a few days old.

They are all busy hunting, grunting softly now and then to say that all is well. They want to have a good meal in the cool of the morning, so they can sleep in comfort through the heat of the day. Here the low juniper and manzanita bushes have been stripped of their berries by other hungry wanderers. No pea pods hang from the desert willow, no beans from the mesquite. They find a few fruit of the prickly pear cactus, passed up by others because of its needlelike spines. For a prickly pear cactus fruit a hungry male will push a young one aside, for these are the peccaries' favorite food. If fruit is scarce above the ground, there are still roots and tubers and

insect larvae to be grubbed up from below. Near a water hole a lucky one may even find a toad, or a low-built bird's nest with tasty eggs.

. Peccaries are not fussy about their food; they like fruits of all kinds, any eggs they can find, lizards, snakes, small animals, roots and grubs.

Now one of the young, long snout to the ground, wanders off beyond the mesquite in pursuit of a flickering lizard. And from nearby a hungry bobcat, holed up for the day in a fallen log's shelter, watches the approach of this tasty meal.

A hungry bobcat

Peccaries on the prowl

Before the baby peccary is near enough for the flattened bobcat to pounce, the mother peccary notices her loss. Now through the peaceful grunting she trumpets a deep note of alarm. At once the team of peccaries responds.

They prefer to run when danger threatens, but now one of their group is about to be attacked! They must go to the wanderer's defense.

The bobcat, planning an easy kill and a delicious meal, more filling than a pocket mouse or ground squirrel, is suddenly aware of a grunting horde clattering toward him on sharp little hoofs. At the same moment, the wind brings him their scent; for when peccaries become excited, the hair stands up on their backs and necks, and the musk glands open on their backs to pour out a few drops (a little bit is plenty) of their own strong, skunk-like fluid.

The bobcat is known around the desert as a vicious fighter who will claw at the eyes or other sensitive part of any enemy that corners him. But even he has no wish to fight a band of peccaries. To begin with—if he took time to think it through—they are bigger; the grown peccaries are just about his length—34 to 40 inches—but they weigh more than twice his 20 pounds, and as he circles cautiously, he can see their gleaming tusks.

The bobcat's instinct is to climb a tree; but in the desert that is easier said than done. The peccaries are between him and the tree-shaded water hole. The only thing at hand is a thorny cactus plant.

Bracing himself for the sting of the spines, up the saguaro he goes. But crash! the cactus breaks under his weight, hurling him to the ground at the feet of his foes!

Once again he takes off in helter-skelter retreat and finds himself a stronger but no less thorny perch. From the lofty top of the saguaro he snarls his rage at the peccaries waiting below.

When he shows no sign of coming down, the peccaries tire of the wait and move along. A chase like that is too hot work with midday coming on. They are ready for a nap.

Diamond-backed rattlesnake

Diamond-Backed Killer

In the desert drama, Nature knows neither hero nor villain. She has provided food for every creature, and to the weaker hunted she has given some defense. She has planned for the survival of all.

The rattlesnake's favorite foods in the desert, it happens, are birds, rats and mice. So nature, in addition to poison-filled fangs, has given him an amazing ability to track his prey.

The rattlesnake has two scent pits above his mouth, so delicate that from the faintest trace of an animal's body warmth left on the sand, he can pick up the faint, invisible trail.

This time it is the trail of a pocket mouse. The tiny

pocket mouse, weighing less than an ounce and measuring only about six inches to the tip of her quivering tail, knows she should not be out hunting food in broad daylight. It is against her safety rules. There are so many dangers in a pocket mouse's life, even in the dark—from snakes and owls and coyotes, skunks, and even from bigger mice. But with babies at home in the burrow, she feels she must lay in as many seeds as possible, against a cold or rainy day.

The babies are quite safe in the burrow, she feels, for its door, beneath a rock overhang in a miniature forest of brush, she closed neatly behind her; and the cozy round sleeping room, lined with bits of grass and weeds

Pocket mouse

is down at the end of a long, steep hall where few marauders could dig. There are side tunnels, too, where her seeds are stored; she is proud of her little home.

But now she is busy stripping the seeds from a creosote bush—and tucking them swiftly, with flying small hands, into her fur-lined cheek pouches. She is too busy to notice the approach of the monster, nose down to sniff her trail.

The rattles warn her! In a flash, with one push of her dainty hands, she empties her pouches of their weight of seeds, and rushes away toward home.

It is not the front door she will enter; no, that would lead the villain to her nest. With swift scoops she uncovers the door to a side tunnel. Down she goes, and her flying feet close it behind her.

On comes the snake, still following the trail. Writhing his four-and-a-half feet of menace along the sand, the snake senses that he is close to his prey; the scent is fresher here.

Pocket mouse meets a tarantula.

Two of the desert's deadliest

On he comes, straight to the hole, he thinks—but out pops a tarantula. Here are two of the desert's deadliest, face to fearful face.

The snake has a huge advantage in size, and he is hungry, too. He does not like to be bluffed out of a meal; he wants to investigate that hole, down which he feels certain the plump mouse dodged.

Nervous and irritable, he rattles his tail. But the tarantula, among the largest of the spiders and deadly in his own right, is quite ready to stand his ground.

And it is the rattlesnake who backs down.

Now the scent is lost. The trail has ended. The rattle-snake sulkily twists away to a sunny resting place. But for the bold black and white of his tail, his color is dull and faded, to suit his background. He is pinkish—showiest of his kind; others may be yellowish or bluish gray. Camouflaged against matching rock, he can rest for a while, digesting his morning meal of baby birds he found in a low-built nest. Or so he thinks.

Across the sky above, unseen by the snake, wheels one of the few desert creatures who care to challenge him. It is the powerful red-tailed hawk.

Down swoops the hawk, his talons stretched, reaching for the head of the snake. But the snake is wary; even without warning, his reactions are those of a coiled steel spring. Down flashes the bird—darting, slashing, taunting, counting on its wings to sweep it up to safety after each thrust.

But the rattlesnake has his powers too. He snatches the creature out of the sky and flings it to the ground, pinning those proud wings to the earth.

The primitive struggle continues; the great wings still flutter; the sleek coils twist.

Suddenly the hawk's beaked head strains around. He seizes the snake's head in jaws of steel. Under this crushing pressure, the snake's struggles are in vain. He thrashes madly for one last moment. Then the boldly patterned coils fall limp. Another desert killer has met his doom.

Red-tailed hawk and rattlesnake
meet in a duel of primitive violence.

As the earth turns
the desert curves
away from the blaze
of the sun. Now the
rays fall obliquely
across the sands,
scattering their heat.
But in the heavens
the clouds catch
the light and
reflect it in wild
sunset glory.

NIGHT IN THE DESERT

Mammals on the Wing

THE DESERT sun is setting behind the mountains, staining the last rock faces it touches with brilliant pinks and gold, trailing lengthening shadows of purple where it can no longer reach.

Sunset is a signal for the red-tailed hawk. No longer can he preen his plumage, resting from his fight with the snake. Every day at sunset, he has a mission. To us it seems a curious one.

Through the gathering darkness he flies each sundown to the same spot—and waits.

The spot is outside the black entrance to a huge cavern.

It is the scene of a strange nightly phenomenon, as regular as clockwork and as mysterious as the stars.

Inside this cavern the bats are awakening—millions upon millions of bats. The great cavern is filled with the squeak of their tiny voices, many of the calls tuned too high for human ears to hear.

During the day they have rested on the roof of the cavern, hanging quietly head down. The mothers have been affectionately caring for the tiny, naked babies clinging to their breasts. When the young bat reaches the age of three weeks, it begins to learn to fly and soon is ready to go on the nightly hunting trips. But during the day its busiest moments will be spent in cleaning itself—licking with its red tongue where it can reach, combing the rest of its fur with tiny feet.

With the coming of darkness, though, the bats' real day begins. Sundown is the signal for their mass flight to their hunting grounds.

It is insects they are hunting, for these bats, the only flying mammal, are nature's counter-balance to the hordes of insects. The millions of bats in this one cavern eat several tons of insects in a night.

Rarely do they dip to the ground in their hunting. They may swoop to a stream for a drink on the wing, but flying insects they snap up with sharp teeth in mid-air or net in the membrane between their back legs.

It is little wonder they stay on the wing, for the bats have a wonderful secret for swift, sure flight.

Bats in flight

The secret of their unerring flights in darkness was long a mystery. The answer, once discovered, proved to be quite simple. Long before man ever thought of it, sonar was a built-in tool for all bats. Like small transmitters, they send out high-pitched sounds, then guide themselves by means of the echoes bouncing off solid objects. With this sure protection, they fly fearlessly through the night.

Now the sky is filled with clouds of bats. Even some of the babies are there, for some mothers, rather than leave them behind, carry the growing children clutched to their breasts—a tremendous weight load for flight! But despite their loads, they go swooping and dipping with the rest, swung about by currents of air. As they pass overhead, they screen the twilight sky.

This is what the red-tailed hawk has been waiting for. He swoops into the clouds of bats to hunt mammals on the wing.

It would seem almost impossible for a hawk to miss with the prey as thick as this. Yet time and again the bats dart away. Their "sonar" warns them of the hawk as a solid object to be dodged.

After many passes, the hawk may catch one. A "collision course," he discovers, feet first into the flying mass, is the most effective approach.

But the loss of one bat, or two—or a dozen—is nothing to Nature. Hundreds of thousands strong, the winged column streams into the sky, long after the last traces of sunlight have faded quite away.

Yet before morning they will be back, each little three- to five-inch creature having caught half its weight in insects on the wing. Back they will go before the daylight, to their dusky perches far below the ground. Each mother who left a tiny baby swinging will find her way back to it. And all across the desert not one will be visible of these strange winged animals who hunt by night.

Bats at home

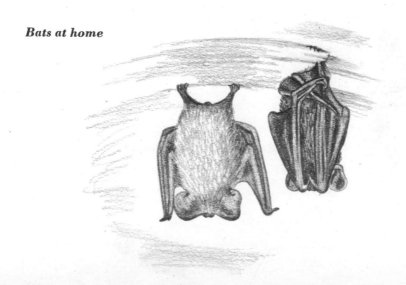

Desert night

At the Waterhole

The night-time wonders of nature's living desert are
rarely seen by human eyes, yet they more than match the
curiosities of the day.

The desert waterhole, in particular, attracts a whole
group of nocturnal creatures who feel safer and better
in the cool dark.

Beside the desert spring is the home of the crusty toad.
Some of his fellows spend most of their lives quietly
buried in the earth, only coming to the surface after a

desert rain. But this fellow, managing to stay near water, has a more active life.

Not that he has to work hard for a dinner. He sits and lets it come to him. His bulging eyes dart this way and that, keeping his small world in view.

He sees a beetle coming, but alas, a tarantula gets it first, crushing its shell to suck the juice.

But there is another beetle. Toad's long tongue zips out

Toad is one of the desert's many nocturnal hunters.

Toad eyeing tasty beetle

from its front hinge. Gulp, the tasty beetle is gone.

Now over a small stone curves a centipede, with its myriad tiny legs a blur of motion—one pair to each segment of its small body. It moves efficiently toward its leafy dinner, until the hairy-legged tarantula scoops it in.

Toad blinks his bulging eyes in disappointment; but this is not a night to be hungry for long. Not far behind the centipede comes the slippery dark form of a "thousand-footed" millipede. The tarantula eyes the millipede too, but the toad has no fear this time. The millipede has two defenses: he can roll himself into a ball, and he can drive many hunters away with his odor. This is enough to discourage the tarantula, but not our toad. Zip goes

Centipede (above) and millipede

his tongue once more, and the millipede vanishes. Now a look of satisfaction seems to glitter in the bulging eyes of the toad.

He watches as the tarantula goes a-courting. Tarantula goes to the burrow door and seems to knock with the nippers he uses to seize and crush his prey.

Down in the burrow she has dug, the lady tarantula waits. She dug it with her rake-like nippers, tossing out the balled dirt with her strong hind feet. She coated it with earth-and-saliva mixture and hung it with a lining of spun silk.

Tarantula knocks on his lady's burrow.

Scorpions join claws as if for a dance.

Now, at the male's knock, she appears in the doorway. At once the male seizes her and draws her close. The lady swoons and the male drags her off.

Toad blinks, as if in boredom with just another desert romance. Oh, he watches them all, just to keep an eye on things. He sees the scorpion digging up his partner from her hiding place beneath the sand, to join claws with her in a stately posture, as if for a dance.

He sees a longhorn beetle come a-courting, his antennae circling around him like a frame. The toad readies his tongue for a strike; any beetle looks good to him.

But the longhorn, who lives beneath the bark of a

dead cottonwood, stops to look in on the beetle below.

She does not welcome his advances. She clamps one of his feelers in her powerful pincers; then she almost bites off his leg.

Now another male appears and attacks our beetle; they battle with pincers locked. When neither seems able to get an advantage, they separate at last. But the female goes off with her other suitor, perhaps to start a family in the cottonwood. For their larvae are borers which live by eating dead or dying wood.

Beetle, who was out looking for adventure, soon finds one of another kind.

Around the next turn in his stony path he meets a

Beetle meets tarantula.

Longhorn beetle

tarantula. Many larger desert folk as brave as he would turn on their heels and run. But not the longhorn beetle.

Nature is on the beetle's side. She gave him some special anti-tarantula weapons—powerful pincer jaws. He fastens them on the tarantula's leg; and when they part, the spider goes on only seven legs, taking with him a new respect for beetles.

On goes Beetle, cockily. Perhaps he feels that he leads a charmed life. But in the moon shadows waits our friend Toad. Out zips his long tongue, and in Beetle goes.

Is that the end? No, not quite. Beetle has one more trick in stock. He bites the toad on his tongue—good and hard—and the unhappy toad spits him out.

Then off goes Beetle, heading for home. He has found enough adventure for one night.

Tiny harvester

Moonlight Harvesters

Under the spiny shelter of a Spanish bayonet, a small doorway lies in deep shadow—black against the violet gray of the desert night.

From underground a small sound echoes faintly—a warning thump, thump, thump. There is a pause, a silence. Then against the blackness of the doorway a small figure appears, neatly furred in pale brown and white, her translucent ears and nose twitching delicately, her eager great dark eyes ashine. She stands erect and tense, alert for any threat, her tiny, pinky-white paws hanging waiting at her sides—but not for long. All is well, so with a flick of her vibrant tail the kangaroo rat bounds off down a faintly beaten trail.

The name "kangaroo," it is plain to see, comes from her long hind legs and the abnormally long, strong tail which acts as a balance as she hops. Actually she is a cousin of the pocket mouse—larger (around 10 inches, counting tail), though not as large as many of her kind. She has the same fur-lined cheek pouches for transporting food supplies, similar coloring, and the pocket mouse's saving ways.

All kangaroo rats have much in common, but it is only these smaller ones which are sociable. Their larger relatives lead hermit-like lives, caring for nothing, so it seems, but harvesting and hoarding quarts, even bushels of seeds. Their burrows are lined with neatly packed pantries, holding many kinds of seeds. They have no use for this smaller, gayer type, who would just as soon borrow from their neighbors' stores as to bother to harvest their own.

The larger kangaroo rats often bury small pockets of seeds just below the surface of the ground, when they have not time to run home with every cheekful. These their smaller cousins are delighted to find.

Mother Rat is off seed-hunting now. She may stop here and there at a neighbor's burrow, to pay a social call. She enjoys seeing friends. They dance with joy at

Kangaroo rats are sociable.

meeting one another, bouncing into the air with sheer good spirits, it seems. And there are many such joyous meetings in a night.

It is only at night that a kangaroo rat would think of venturing out. Even bright moonlight may keep her at home, unless her babies are in real need of food. For the world is full of dangers, and the kangaroo rat feels safer in the sheltering dark.

She can bounce along swiftly in jumps twice her own length; she can zigzag, turning sharply on her tail, which confuses many enemies. She has sharp eyes, keen ears, and a sensitive nose to warn her of danger, but still she likes to have darkness on her side, too.

There is plenty to keep her busy all day. Homemaking is not a simple job for any kangaroo rat. First of all a burrow must be dug, with hard-packed tunnels and high, round rooms where one can comfortably sit up straight. For safety, the burrow must have many entrances, and it is wise to keep changing them, letting one drift full here, and digging a new one there. There must be some blind alleys to mislead enemies, and several twisting paths leading to the nest, softly lined with fine grass, weed silk and feathers.

Even when the burrow is quite finished, and a family of babies lies curled in the downy nest, the work at home is never done. There is always a wall collapsing between passages dug too close; or a wandering enemy on the surface puts a foot through a passage roof. A hungry coyote or snake may come rooting down a hall; or a toad or lizard may wander in and settle down, quite uninvited, to make himself at home. Mother Rat never seems to catch up with her housekeeping, even though she is not one of the thrifty, seed-hoarding type.

Today, in the midst of her busy schedule, she has had a real fright. She had just finished feeding the babies

Bouncing with sheer good spirits

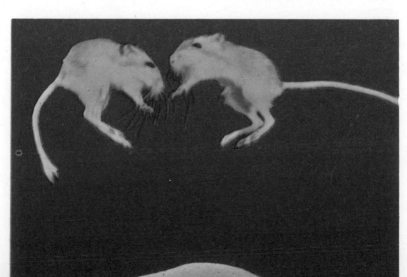

when she heard a scrabbling at the door. At once she stopped and thumped a warning with one of her strong hind feet. She waited a moment. The scrabbling sound continued. Once again she thumped. But was this an enemy who could not be frightened? She picked up a baby, gripping the loose skin of its neck firmly in her teeth. For a moment she waited, ready to speed up a ramp to a safer burrow. But the scrabbling stopped. Her tiny nose quivered, but could catch no scent of an enemy's approach. After another moment of silence she began to feel quite safe again. She put the baby back in the nest, and settled down to work. One danger was past.

Now, even in the safety of darkness, at first she hesitates to go too far from home. Coming upon a group of neighborhood mothers—there are 200 rats in this community—she pauses for a visit and a dust bath.

Like all kangaroo rats, she is very neat, and loves to be well groomed. Grooming does not mean a water bath to her; she hates water and never ventures out when it rains. She bathes in dust or powdery sand; and she grooms herself by distributing the oil from glands on her back evenly through her fur.

Water means little in her life. Oh, a sip of a dew drop now and then is fine; but what water a kangaroo rat's system needs he (or she) manufactures within his body from dry foods.

This food is mostly seeds—preferably crisp and dry. Mrs. Rat sees a likely-looking seed pod now. Having finished her grooming, she bounces toward it, lifting her tiny hands. Spat! comes a flick of sand in her face. Another rat has beaten her to these seeds, and is standing by his claim.

Off bounces Mrs. Rat, to another stand of grasses. Soon her cheeks are puffing out with seeds. Nibble, nibble—busy with her harvest, she does not at first notice the approach of another shadowy figure in the night. It is the king snake, not poisonous to humans but deadly to kangaroo rats none the less, because they are a favorite food of his.

Stealthily, silently, up he steals. He coils in the darkness—two and a half feet of scaly pale yellow, marked with rings of black and white. Those coils can tighten

Kangaroo rat's dust bath

around a victim, winding close and closer still, until the little life is squeezed out.

Now he lunges toward the mother rat! But thanks to her sandy coloring against the darkness, the big snake misses. The terrified mother does not give him another chance. Home she races to save her babies. As she feared, the snake follows her.

She has not a moment to lose! Down a hole she darts, through a maze of twisting tunnels, to the nest where the babies wait. Up another hole she comes with a baby, and vanishes down an extra burrow with it. Up she comes again, and starts home for the second.

Now the snake has followed her to the door she used

King snakes can follow the slightest trail.

Gecko lizard has a replaceable tail.

first. As the little mother hurries down a second tunnel, the snake is sliding his hungry black snout in the first, hunting for the plump, tender baby.

Mother rescues her second baby in the nick of time; but now they must go out again, into the open where the enemy waits. Up the farthest tunnel she races with the baby. But inside the black doorway she stops.

At this moment, along comes a friend in need, the harmless gecko lizard. He attracts the eye of the hungry snake as it backs out from the mother rat's burrow.

Poor gecko! The king snake does not miss this time. He pulls off the lizard's tail in one bite. But the sturdy gecko does not collapse, not a bit of it. Nature has given him a handy defense, a detachable, replaceable tail. He will not miss the one he has lost. He will soon grow another and be as good as new.

Thanks to friend gecko, Mother Rat has time to dart into the extra burrow with her second baby, too. There in the nest she rests for a moment, until her tiny heart stops its pounding from the narrow escape.

When she ventures out into the night again, she notices some sort of excitement at the top of a sandy rise. With her babies tucked safely away, she hops over for a look.

The same rat who frightened her away from the seeds has found himself another adventure, it seems. In his wanderings he has come upon the track of a horned rattlesnake, called a sidewinder because of his twisting, side-wise gait.

Like his larger cousin, the diamond-backed rattle-snake, the sidewinder is a formidable hunter, and small rodents—rats and mice—are his favorite food.

Nature has given him a hunting territory all his own. For his method of traveling, by swinging himself along sideways, loop after loop, permits him to go through soft sand where other snakes cannot go.

He does not bother to track down his prey, as other rattlesnakes do. He waits for it to come to him, as this kangaroo rat has done. Up came the busy rat, twitching nose to the ground.

But before the snake had a chance to strike, the rat spied his enemy. He jumped high into the air in surprise. Then, instead of turning to run, he whirled about and

The sidewinder loops himself across the sand.

Kangaroo rat, surprised by sidewinder.

kicked up sand in a swift, hard spatter at the snake.

The stinging grains bounced harmlessly from the snake's tough scales; but still his head turned uneasily. It was his eyes which were bothering him, for they had no lids; he could not close them against the flying grains. Under their peaked horns his eyes were almost defenseless; he could not even squint. True, they had a filmy protection of a sort, but it was not defense against an attack like this.

For now others (including Mrs. Rat), were coming on

the bound to join the attack against the enemy. With sharp sand grains flying at him from all sides, the snake could do little but retreat. Over the hill he swiftly went, looping his sidewise way along.

The moment the enemy was out of sight, the victory celebration began. What a jolly rumpus the little rats made, dancing and jumping and bouncing about, with rough little play battles and bird-like twitterings.

Like most noisy parties, this one wakes the neighbors. And the neighbors are a hungry lot. From her near-by

A spatter of sand overcomes the snake.

den comes the ringtail cat, a great admirer of kangaroo rats, as food. She is really no more a cat than her cousin, the raccoon; but she does have two cat-like features: she can see in the dark and she likes to eat plump rats. Now her big, round, dark eyes dance with excitement at the sight of this possible feast.

As the ringtail watches the merry goings-on, thinking perhaps of the hungry squeakings of her kitten-sized

Ringtail cat

Owls feast on small rodents, too.

young at home, another spectator happens by—owl, who relishes rodents, too.

For one more moment the party continues. Then, in a single flash, the owl pounces, the cat leaps, the rats bounce to safety—and for this time get away.

Down the steep tunnel of her second burrow scampers Mother Rat. She brushes past a sleepy lizard, waiting for the sun, and rounds the last turn leading to the nest. There are her babies, sound asleep, safe and sweet as when she left. She curls up beside them, letting all her tense little senses relax at last.

It is time now for her to rest again, without a worry as to what the next day may bring.

Morning Games

Over the desert the night sky pales and brightens. Quietly the creatures of the night disappear into their hidden homes. When the first light of dawn catches fire on the tips of the guardian mountain peaks, they have vanished quite away.

With the sunrise, in the cool of the early morning, the first creatures of the day appear. Along the fringes of the desert, close to the beds of streams, the round-tail

ground squirrels are early risers, soberly hunting their breakfast — and something for their winter stores.

Up the hard-packed tunnels of their burrows they come, up from the dark comfort of their grass-carpeted nest chambers. Some may take the shorter back tunnels to their burrow's hidden second doors. But once on the surface they leap lightly over the ground, to avoid leaving trails to lead enemies home.

Some nibble daintily on cactus, expertly avoiding the dagger-sharp spines. The cactus is both food and drink to them; from its juices they get all the moisture they need. Others eat mesquite beans and seed pods. All the varied members of the pea family—second only to the cacti among desert plants—the mesquite, the palo verde, the smoke tree, cat's claw acacia, and desert ironwood, are favorites of theirs.

Eating is serious business for the ground squirrels. When one skinny little fellow finishes his meal and starts racing in and out of the group, nudging the others, trying to start a game of tag, they look coldly upon him. When their patience runs out—and they are not patient folks— the other squirrels pile on him and give him the pummeling they think he deserves.

Then back go the squirrels to their seed harvest. They may carry home as many as a hundred tiny seeds at a time to hide away. Or they hollow out small crannies under handy rocks or logs, and store their seed stocks there. It is everyone for himself among the ground squirrels; for they never seem to share their homes or food. Now they are soberly back at work, eating fruits they cannot store away, sometimes climbing high up bending stems after seeds they especially want.

They do not give a thought to the stranger they handled so rudely. He wanders around feeling just a bit sad. So it happens that he is the first to spy an enemy, and a dangerous one, as a Gila monster rounds a rock.

The Gila monster is a queer combination of beauty and ugliness. He rather resembles a beaded bag, but his bright, almost circus-like appearance is pure deception; for in his lower jaw is a gland from which poison flows, through his grooved teeth, when he bites.

When the newcomer whistles his short, sharp warning, the squirrels are quick to heed the alarm. In the flurry

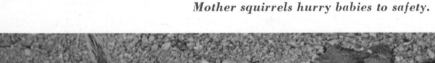

Mother squirrels hurry babies to safety.

Gila monster has a grim beauty.

of excitement, their chirrup of chattering rises to shrill cries, as everybody scampers every which way. Mothers grab up their young and carry them down into burrows, for they know that the bite of this venomous lizard means certain death. Squirrels who are old enough to look after themselves scamper up into bushes—though they would rather go underground than climb—or perch precariously on slender, nodding weeds which threaten to spill them at the enemy's feet.

Something must be done about this alarming lizard. But no one seems to care to try. At this point, up bobs the scrawny stranger. He is as ready to tackle a monster as he was for a game of tag. On comes the monster, looking mighty threatening, but the cocky squirrel is not impressed. He has his own method for jobs like this.

His method of dealing with Gila monsters is simply to insult them. He sidles up to the monster and scoops up dirt in his face. The lizard snaps at him, but the squirrel is nimble. He seems to count on the lizard's clumsiness, and approaches within a flick of the Gila monster's wicked-looking black tongue.

Spat! comes more sand. The lizard hesitates. That is all the encouragement the ground squirrel needs. Though the other squirrels chatter warnings at him, he keeps bravely on hurling brisk pawloads of sandy dirt, until the Gila monster cannot take it any more. He ambles away. And the newcomer is the hero of the day.

The monster is frightened away.

Roadrunners peck at anything—even snakes.

No sooner are the other squirrels back at their work, chatting amiably among themselves, than another stranger happens by. He is an odd character indeed—a bird who would rather walk than fly, the roadrunner by name. He has a bold and curious habit of pecking at almost anything he happens upon.

Now it is a small harmless snake. Peck, snip, off comes the snake's tail. That is the roadrunner's idea of fun. The snake is not amused. He coils like a rattler, looking as fierce as he can. But the roadrunner is not frightened. He simply skitters on, looking for something new to peck and nibble at.

Ground squirrels are business-like harvesters.

The next thing he spies is the group of ground squirrels, back at their business of picking seeds. Up darts the roadrunner, peck, peck, peck! He nips the brave and cocky little squirrel, tail and nose. But a ground squirrel who has bested a Gila monster is not to be treated this way. Having frightened a giant, he won't take this from a clown. He turns on the roadrunner and bites him back!

Away goes the roadrunner, speedily out of sight. Having his own joke played on him is a thing few clowns can stand.

The squirrels are no sooner rid of one nuisance than another appears. This one seems to have a grudge against

everybody, or so the squirrels think. The spotted skunk
is the smallest of the skunks, and daintily playful with
his friends. His size is about the same as the ground
squirrel's—ranging around 18 inches in length, including
a lot of tail, with a weight from 1 to 2 pounds; but his diet
includes young ground squirrels and such, so he is not
welcome here.

He has another habit which makes him less than
welcome in many groups—such as the nest of young bobcats he has just left. That is his way of standing on his
hands—sometimes in play or just as a bluff, but sometimes
in deadly seriousness. And when the spotted skunk is
being seriously unfriendly, no one wants to be around.

Spotted skunk visits young bobcats.

For he has two glands beneath his tail from which he can shoot a spray of oily liquid extremely sharp and unpleasant in smell, and very clinging too! The spotted skunk does not always spray from his hand-stand. Unless his target is high up, he sprays from his usual standing position.

The squirrels know all this: they do not want to argue with him. They keep their babies out of reach, and the spotted skunk soon ambles along his lonely way. It is time for him to be bedding down, for he is really a night hunter, but this once he has stayed out late into the day. He is not one to want to make trouble, though, in spite of what others may think. He is a long way from his home, and he just wants to find a warm and cozy nest with some friends, for a good day's sleep.

Skunk's handstand is a warning to neighbors.

THE TALE OF THE PEPSIS WASP

ONE of the strangest dramas of the desert is the mortal combat of the pepsis wasp with the dread tarantula. A hint of the plot is given in the wasp's common name; she is often called the tarantula hawk.

Her story is one of the most fantastic in all the strange lore of the desert. It is a tale of a mother who, to provide for her unborn young, risks a terrible death.

When the time comes for the pepsis wasp to lay an egg, she does not prepare a nest, as so many females do. Instead, she goes hunting. Instinct sends her searching out a great venomous spider, the tarantula.

On this morning a wasp is undertaking this solemn mission. It is not a matter of thought or choice; she is obeying an instinct too obscure to be understood and too strong to be questioned.

She is carrying out one of the strangest of nature's many

and varied designs planned to insure the survival of a species.

Her first problem is just to find a tarantula. She thrusts her head into the first likely-looking hole she sees; but there is no one there. She tries the second, looking for trouble, one might almost say. And this time she finds it! Not a tarantula, but a colony of ants who swarm out to the attack. These attackers are so small she can't possibly sting each one. To fight her way out of their clutches is almost too much for the wasp.

To the ants, the pepsis wasp represents a banquet for the whole colony, if only they can bring her to earth. So out they stream, and clutch at her wings, clinging in heavy clumps to her legs, weighing her down so she cannot fly. Poor wasp! She struggles, but in vain it seems.

Still she does not give up; and at last with a frantic effort she shakes herself loose. Free of the ants, she dusts herself off and resumes her search again.

Another hole, another poke—and this time her reward is a tarantula.

Out lumbers the tarantula, and spies the tasty-looking wasp. Now the odd battle begins—the wasp's skill against the spider's great advantage in size.

They spar cautiously for an opening—and the spider makes the first thrust. The wasp is quick to return the blow—and is bitten in the exchange.

Before the spider's poison can take effect, the wasp rubs her body briskly in the sand, as if she found healing

there. This takes her out of the battle for a moment. If the spider followed up her advantage now, the battle might be ended, the wasp's hopes crushed.

The spider, however, is slow to take advantage of the opportunity. Instead of rushing in, she stands aside, holding her body high out of reach. For her abdomen is the only part on which the wasp's poison would have effect.

The wasp senses this. Back in the fray she begins an odd series of maneuvers to get into position for the death blow. To avoid the spider's fangs and to strike herself, the wasp must finally lie on her back and attack from below.

Zing, zing, zing! She plunges her stinger home in the undefended abdomen of the tarantula. Gradually her repeated stings take effect. The spider is gradually slowing down, as the poison seeps through her system; she reels away a step, obviously groggy. The wasp delivers her final stings in a frantic orgy of rage. She must sting her victim enough times so that the spider is completely paralyzed and unable to resist.

With that the second phase of her strange task is done. She has found her victim, and she has fought it into complete submission. Next she must drag its limp and heavy body to a place where she can bury it— though she might call it preparing a nest for her young.

When she has chosen a secret spot, despite the exhausting battle she has been through, she begins to dig

frantically. As soon as the hole is sizable, she drags the spider over to try it for fit; the excavation is still too small. She digs again, dragging out pebbles larger than she is, until she can haul the spider down into the combination nest and tomb.

The spider is not dead but paralyzed. The wasp buries it, but before she covers over the hole, she lays an egg, and only one, on the spider's body. The preserved spider then provides a supply of fresh food for the pepsis wasp's baby, when the larva hatches from the egg in this strange nest.

Before the wasp larva is full grown, it will have consumed all the edible parts of this great tarantula.

The pepsis wasp is the largest of American wasps, and one of the most striking, with blue-black body and wings of brilliant orange. But it is not the only one to use this strange plan for infant care. Most wasps, whether of a solitary type, like the pepsis, or a social sort who live in colonies, stock the cells where they lay their eggs with insects or spiders of some sort, to provide the larvae with food.

For each and every egg this pepsis wasp lays, she must find and overcome a new tarantula. For the moment now, having covered up the nest, she can wander off and relax. But then she must look for another spider, and another fight which may as easily end for her in death as in victory. That is her fate, and the pepsis wasp knows no other way of life.

DESERT BLOOM

THE LIVING desert knows death and destruction, but it knows rejuvenation and birth as well.

As the tarantula hawk completes her work, smoothing over the entrance to her victim's tomb, black clouds begin to pile up on the distant horizon. One of the rare desert rainstorms is on the way.

Though for months on end the dry sands swirl and the gullied banks of river beds crumble into dust, in due time nature ends the drought, and sends storm clouds filled with promise sweeping over this thirsty land.

Of course in this land of extremes there are few soft showers, few slow and gentle rains. Halfway measures in

Under the wild
assault of the rain
the parched desert
lies as if stunned.
Sand, stones,
even rock walls
crumble and slide
away before the rush
of wild waters.
But when the rain
has ceased,
the spent pools lie
exhausted in hollows
reflecting the sky.

Desert rainbow

the desert are uncommon. When it does rain, nature may deluge the thirsty earth with a cloudburst. Sometimes a third of the annual rainfall comes down within a few hours of one day.

Down falls a blanket, a curtain of water, hiding the landscape from sight. But as suddenly as it came, the storm passes. The glory of the desert rainbow appears.

The pools that mirror the brilliance of the sky soon run off down the sloping surfaces, or seep away, vanishing in the sand. From the bare hills the water runs off swiftly, since no web of roots and foliage holds it back. All trace of the rain, it seems, is soon gone.

But wait! Miles away, under a cloudless sky, a rumbling like muffled thunder is heard. It is an eerie sound; it seems to echo from all the canyons at once. It is closer now, a louder, living roar. And suddenly, as if from nowhere, bursts the flash flood of the desert.

Mounting in fury as it races down the draws, sweeping everything before it, a wall of water advances. Away go soil and shrubs and sand; down the tiny tunnels hard-packed by tiny feet, the flood pours deadly fingers, and into the sheltered nests.

It grows in size and force, in speed and dreadful power. It is a raging river, a desert Niagara. Its roar fills the air, dazzling the ears. It is a monster; it is upon us . . . It is gone.

In all these stretching miles of space, there is nowhere for a lost river to go. No bed is firm enough to channel its flow. Its currents fan out over the sandy flats; its source in the hills runs dry.

Flash flood

The thirsty earth clutches greedily at the water. Soon only a river of mud remains. And even that last sluggish reminder of the once-raging torrent is swallowed up in the desert's vastness as the river sinks into earth again.

The sun soon dries out the last bit of moisture. Cracks appear in the parched ground. It is almost as if the rain had never been.

But more was accomplished by that rain than at first meets the eye. The desert is a storehouse of dormant, resting seeds, waiting only for moisture to burst into bloom.

A wonderland of blossom follows the rain.

Joshua tree in blossom

Devil's finger (top) and night-blooming cereus

Some of them, like the tiny belly plant (which you must lie flat on the ground to see) will wait dormant ten years, if necessary, for the right amount of rain.

Now, under the raindrops' magic touch, almost over-night it seems the desert bursts into glory. Once again Nature tolerates no half-way measures. Her bounty of beauty is abundant beyond all imagination.

Her desert primrose contributes delicacy to the scene, her lupine and golden poppy, extravagant color. Still none can surpass the cactus blossoms for startling beauty of form and color. Nature seems to take her greatest pride in this, that from these dwarfed and twisted plants, blunted and bowed by the hardship of barely staying alive, she brings this perfect loveliness.

It is a swiftly passing beauty, this miracle of the desert flowers; for a few brief days it transforms this

Beavertail cactus

Prickly pear cactus   *Saguaro*

drab setting into a colorful garden. Then the fragile blossoms must wilt and die. The starkness of the desert will reclaim its own.

But this climax of one of Nature's richest patterns was not beauty for beauty's sake alone. Nature as always had the future in view; the blossoms die but not before the soil has been sown with seeds—dormant seeds that will recreate this miracle in seasons to come. For Nature's design for the desert is a permanent one. Nature preserves her work, and over the long eternity of time perpetuates one of her greatest miracles—the endless wonder of the Living Desert.

Pincushion cactus

Giant saguaro

A CAST OF DESERT CHARACTERS

ant—an insect of the same order as the bee and the wasp. The ant is a social insect and lives in colonies varying from a few dozen to hundreds of thousands. Each colony has one or more egg-laying queens, other females who are wingless workers, and some winged males.

armadillo—a burrowing mammal whose head and body are almost entirely covered by long, horny scales. Its food is largely insects. More armadillos live in South America than in North America, and only the nine-banded armadillo is found in the United States.

bat—the only mammal which really flies. Its wings are not feathered, but are membranes stretched between what could be called the four fingers of the bat's forepaws. Of course, the fingers have become very long. Bats usually hang head-down in caves or other dark places when at rest. They are found in almost all sections of the world but the very cold ones.

beetle—any of an order of insects of about 22,000 species in North America alone. Each beetle starts life as an egg and turns into a wormlike larva or grub. It goes through a resting stage before it becomes an adult beetle, with two pairs of wings. One pair is really a sturdy protective set of wing covers which fit over the body and other pair.

bobcat—a kind of lynx, also called the wildcat. He has tufted ears and a short tail, and is usually about 36 inches long with thick yellow and brown fur, which is striped down the back with black. He hunts at twilight and feeds on mice, birds, squirrels, and other small prey. The bobcat nests in trees or rocks, and the female usually has 2 to 4 young.

borer—any of the insect larvae, as of beetles and horntails, that bore into the bark and wood of trees and into other plants. Some insects have a special organ, called the ovipositor, with which they bore holes to place eggs within the wood of trees.

centipede — a worm-like, segmented relative of the insects, 1 to 8 inches long, having long antennae and numerous legs.

chuckwalla—a large, harmless, plant-eating lizard of the southwestern states which used to be enjoyed as food by the Indians.

coati mundi—a brown-coated animal related to the raccoon, but having a longer body and tail, and a long, flexible snout.

coyote—a small variety of wolf, also called prairie wolf, having rough, gray fur, a sharp, dog-like face, and a long, bushy tail. The coyote is often found on the desert, where it feeds on small animals and on mesquite and juniper seeds.

desert tortoise — sometimes called "Agassiz's tortoise," attaining a length of about 9 inches and a width of 6 inches. It survives the dryness of the desert by storing liquid in two sacks beneath its shell.

diamond-backed rattlesnake— a poisonous, thick-bodied snake having joints at the end of the tail which make a rattling or buzzing sound. The snake is named for the diamond-shaped markings on its back.

finch—see *house finch.*

flycatcher—any of a family of small perching birds which feed on insects taken during flight.

garter snake — a small, harmless American snake which has two or three yellow stripes running along its back from head to tail.

gecko lizard—a variety of small lizard found in the western United States. It is characterized by a brittle tail which breaks off when bitten by an enemy. The tail is replaceable through normal growth.

Gila monster — largest of the American lizards (up to 22 inches). This black-and-orange Sonoran desert inhabitant is the only poisonous lizard found in the United States.

ground squirrel—a small, buff-colored member of the squirrel family which lives in the desert. It makes its home in a burrow, or under bushes and shrubs.

grubs—worm-like larvae, such as those of the beetle family.

hawk, red-tailed — a large, brown, soaring bird of prey with a short, round, red-topped tail. It attacks its prey by diving from high altitudes and snatching animals with its sharp claws or talons.

horned rattlesnake—see *sidewinder.*

house finch—a sparrow-sized,

tan western bird, the male with red breast and rump, which often nests in the branches of cacti.

insect—any member of a class of small, boneless animals having three separate body parts—head, thorax, and abdomen—and six legs. This group includes at least 600,000 winged and crawling animals.

kangaroo rat—one of the larger varieties of desert rodent. Its long tail and large hind legs enable it to make prodigious jumps. The kangaroo rat is a larger cousin of the pocket mouse, and is often 10 inches long.

king snake — a medium-sized, non-poisonous snake. It kills prey by strangulation. The king snake usually is not harmed by the venom of poisonous snakes, and sometimes kills and swallows rattlesnakes.

lizard—any of a group of small reptiles characterized by long tapering bodies and scaly skins, and sometimes by four short legs.

longhorn beetle — a beetle which has long, flexible antennae, and powerful pincers with which it captures other insects for food. It is brown and usually an inch in length.

mammal—any animal which is warm-blooded, bears its young alive, and feeds its offspring milk, and usually has a hair-covered body.

millipede—a small, many-legged creature which has many body segments, and two pairs of legs on most segments.

mouse—see *pocket mouse.*

omnivore—any animal which eats both animal and vegetable food.

owl — a bird of prey distinguished by large eyes, a wide head, extremely sharp talons, and nocturnal habits.

peccary—an American wild pig, generally about 36 inches long, which has sharp hooves, coarse-haired coat, and a peculiar musk gland. The gland gives off a pungent odor, something like that of a skunk.

pepsis wasp—a beautiful black-and-red wasp which uses tarantulas in order to provide food for its young. It lays its eggs on the bodies of tarantulas it has paralyzed by its sting. As wasp larvae develop, they feed on the tarantulas. Because of its almost unique ability to overcome the tarantulas, the pepsis wasp is also known as the tarantula hawk.

pocket mouse—a member of

the rodent order, 5 inches in length, which is distinguished by the small pockets on the inside of its mouth where food is carried.

rat—see *kangaroo rat*.

rattlesnake—any of a group of poisonous snakes that have tail-joints which vibrate and produce a rattling sound.

red racer—a fast-moving, reddish-brown snake of the non-poisonous variety.

ringtail cat—a small, cat-like animal of the desert, which has a pointed face, large eyes, and the striped tail which gives it its name.

roadrunner — a long, slender, shaggy-crested bird having a long beak and powerful legs which give it great speed in running. It prefers running to flying.

rodent — any of an order of mammals distinguished by a pair of enlarged incisor teeth in the upper and lower jaws. The order includes rats, mice, squirrels, beavers, and porcupines.

scorpion—any of an order of animals that have an elongated, hard-shelled body, jointed legs, and a pair of strong pincers. The scorpion has a venomous sting in the end of the tail.

sidewinder—a species of rattle-snake, so named because of its sidewise motion when traveling. The snake is also known as the horned rattlesnake because of the knob on each side of the fore part of its head.

skunk—a black-and-white striped animal having a musk sac which produces a strong, unpleasant smell when the animal is aroused.

snake—any of a group of elongated reptiles lacking limbs and ear openings. Some snakes are highly poisonous; these inject their venom into victims through hollow fangs.

spider—see *tarantula*.

spotted skunk—skunk whose stripes are broken and appear as spots.

tarantula—a large, hairy spider whose poisonous bite can prove very painful to animals and humans alike.

tarantula hawk—see *pepsis wasp*.

thrasher—a long-tailed, robin-sized singing bird which has a gray-brown body and a striped or spotted breast.

toad—a tailless leaping amphibian of the frog family.

tortoise—see *desert tortoise*.

wasp—see *pepsis wasp*.

woodpecker — a type of bird whose sharp-pointed beak penetrates tree bark in search of food. In the desert, some species of woodpecker are black, with white under-bodies. Gila wood- peckers make their nests in certain cactus plants, and hollow nests out of the large saguaro cactus.

ANIMAL TERMS

antenna—the pair of sensitive "feelers" that grow from the head of adult insects. Antennae are sensory organs of hearing and smell, as well as of touch. The antennae may be long and thin, crooked, knobbed, or of other shapes. They are movable and in segments.

cheek pouch—a sac-like pocket in the mouth of certain rodents, such as the pocket mouse. The pocket is used for holding food until it can be eaten or stored. The pocket is sometimes fur-lined.

claw—a pincer or nipper, as in scorpions; also, a sharp toenail on other animals.

fangs—long, sharp teeth with which animals tear, seize, or hold their prey. Also, one of the long, curved, hollow, or grooved, sometimes erectile teeth of a poisonous snake.

fossil—an impression, cast, or other trace of an ancient animal or plant naturally preserved in rock.

grooming—the act of distributing the body oil through the fur, as practiced by certain members of the rodent order.

membrane—a thin, soft, pliable tissue that covers certain parts of plants and animals.

musk glands—small, scent-producing organs beneath the skin, with openings along the back, of certain animals. They produce a strong skunk-like smell.

nippers—sharp claws or pincers found on a number of animals such as the scorpion and the beetle.

pincers—see *nippers*.

scales — small, flattened plates which serve as skin-covering for fish and reptiles.

sting—the hollow, needle-like part of an animal, as the wasp or scorpion, which delivers venomous fluid into the bodies of its enemies.

transmitter—any mechanism which is capable of sending physical energy. The vocal apparatus of the bat is the transmitter of high-pitched sounds which, when echoed, guide the animal in flight.

SOME DESERT PLANTS AND FLOWERS

barrel cactus—a group of cactus plants having cylindrical, barrel-like, spiny stems containing spongy tissues for water storage. They grow to 8 feet in height, and bear orange or yellow blossoms.

cactus—a family of plants with fleshy green stems and branches, and with spines and scales instead of leaves. Cactus plants are found almost exclusively in the western hemisphere. A few species grow to be 30 or 40 feet high. Their large stems, filled with spongy tissue, and absence of leaves, make them well suited to desert life.

cat's-claw acacia—a common straggling shrub or small tree often forming dense thickets along desert washes. Branches are armed with curved thorns resembling the claws of a cat.

cholla—an unusually spiny tree-like form of cactus found in the desert.

cottonwood—a type of poplar tree so named because of the cottony coating around its seeds.

creosote bush—a common evergreen shrub whose leaves have a pungent, musty odor. It stands 2 to 5 feet high, has black-ringed stems, and bears yellow blossoms in early spring or following rain.

desert holly—a shrubby desert saltbush whose silvery, evergreen leaves are gathered for Christmas decorations and winter bouquets and are sometimes dyed or gilded. Because of this destruction, the plant is becoming increasingly rare, and may disappear from the desert.

desert ironwood or **tesota**—a tree which grows to a height of 30 feet. It has dense leaves, fragrant pea-like flowers, and a drought-resistant bark.

desert willow—a small tree of the catalpa family. It bears small pink or orchid-colored flowers and a fruit resembling the string bean.

hedgehog cactus—a short, cucumber-shaped cactus so named because its spines resemble porcupine quills.

holly—see *desert holly*.

Joshua tree—a member of the lily family, sometimes called the yucca tree. It grows 25 feet tall, with twisting branches, and has greenish-white flowers.

juniper—an evergreen tree having blunt, scale-like leaves and blue berries. The berry-like cones of the juniper provide food for birds and small animals of the desert.

lupine—flower of the pea family which grows wild in the western United States. It may be blue, pink, white or, rarely, yellow. Sometimes called bluebonnet.

manzanita—an evergreen shrub of the heath family which grows to a maximum height of 12 feet. The manzanita has reddish bark, crooked branches, and bears small brown berries which give it the Spanish name "little apple."

mesquite — a spiny flowering shrub of the *Prosopis* genus which bears 4- to 8-inch-long pods, somewhat like string beans.

organ cactus — a cactus of northern Mexico and southwestern Arizona, with clusters of greatly elongated, unbranched, ridged stems, sometimes 15 to 18 feet long.

palo verde — a slow-growing

tree whose maximum height is 25 feet. It is covered with yellow flowers in late spring and has green bark. The words *palo verde* are Spanish for green stick.

pincushion cactus—a low cactus whose shape and sharp spines suggest a pincushion.

prickly-pear cactus—a cactus which has flat-jointed stems and an edible, pear-shaped fruit.

primrose—a large desert wildflower which blooms only after rainfall.

sage—a whitish shrub of the aster family, abundant on the plains of western United States.

saguaro—one of the largest of cactus plants. It is tree-like in shape and sometimes grows to a height of 50 feet.

smoke tree—a large shrub, or small, graceful tree, whose grayish, feathery foliage resembles, at a distance, a wisp of smoke from a tall fire.

Spanish bayonet — a type of yucca which derives its name from its sharp leaves, which look like swords.

spines — stiff, sharp-pointed stickers found on many plants, particularly those of the cactus family.

willow—see *desert willow*.

yucca tree—see *Joshua tree*.

DESERT TERMS AND PLACE NAMES

abrasion—the wearing down of rocks by friction, principally with sand particles.

arroyo—a watercourse, usually dry, which has been carved into a gulley by erosion.

Atacama—the great desert of South America in northern Chile. It is rich in nitrates and copper. It lies between coastal mountains and the Andes Mountains, which cut off moisture-laden clouds so completely that in some areas rain has never been recorded.

Bad Water — the lowest geographical point in the United States, 280 feet below sea level. Bad Water is a series of alkaline pools located in Death Valley National Monument in southeastern California.

burrows—holes in the ground made by certain animals for protection and to use as homes.

canyon — a deep valley, with rocky, steep slopes, generally found in the western United States.

Cascade Mountains—a northern continuation of the Sierra Nevada range, extending 500 miles through northern California, Oregon and Washington.

chapparal — a type of plant community where shrubs and small trees predominate, as in parts of the desert.

cloudburst—a sudden, violent, and generally short-lived fall of rain.

Death Valley—a deep, arid basin surrounded by the Panamint and Funeral mountain ranges. Death Valley contains the lowest point in the United States, 280 feet below sea level. It extends from southeastern California into southern Nevada.

dunes—hills or ridges of sand piled up by the winds.

"dust devils" — small whirlwinds which pick up dust and swirl across the desert.

erosion — the slow wearing away of the earth's surface by water in motion, by ice, and by blown dust.

flash flood—a sudden, rapidly moving accumulation, in a narrow canyon, of water resulting from a short, heavy rainfall over a considerable area draining into a single canyon. Such floods rushing down dry watercourses are usually unexpected and may be very dangerous.

Gobi—the 500,000-square-mile desert which lies in China and Mongolia. The desert can support few men and animals, and is usually only traveled by camel caravan.

gorge — a narrow cut in the earth, often caused by long years of erosion, and sometimes extending to hundreds of feet in depth.

Great American Desert — an arid region of the Southwest, extending eastward from the Sierra Nevadas to western Texas and from Nevada and Utah into Mexico. Composed of the Great Basin, Mojave, Sonoran, and Chihuahuan deserts.

mirage—in the desert sky, an image (often inverted) of an object or area which is actually on the earth's surface. It is due to the refraction, or bending, of light rays from the object by successive layers of air of unequal temperature and density. Typically, the light rays from the object are deflected upward toward the sky, then downward toward the observer. The shimmering effect produced by refraction of light rays may also cause the observer to think he sees a distant body of water.

Mojave Desert—an arid basin in southern California, ranging from Los Angeles county to San Bernardino county.

Monument Valley—an area in northern Arizona and southern Utah containing spectacular and immense erosional remnants that resemble pillars and monuments.

Mount Whitney — the highest mountain in the United States, with a peak that reaches 14,496 feet above sea level. Mount Whitney is located in the Sierra Nevada range, along the western border of the Great American Desert.

mudpots—natural wells of boiling mud which erupt continually and emit steam.

passage—any avenue, opening, or route from one point to another. Also, a tunnel or underground pathway, such as those built by rats and mice.

Petrified Forest — an area in Arizona littered with the remnants of ancient fallen trees. These, while buried for a long period, had their tissues replaced by minerals. Later the covering material eroded away, exposing the mineralized trunks.

ramp—an incline or slope, such as that leading from an animal's burrow to the surface of the ground.

sandstorm—storms of high wind in which quantities of sand are picked up from the desert surface and blown with great force.

Sierra Nevada—a mountain range in eastern California which includes the 14,496-foot Mount Whitney, the highest point in the United States.

sonar—a method or device for determining ocean depths or locating underwater objects. Sounds emitted by a transmitter travel to the ocean bottom and are echoed back to the receiver, and the elapsed time indicates the depth. In the same way when sounds emitted by the transmitter are echoed back by any neighboring objects, the direction from which the echo comes indicates the direction of the object, and the elapsed time indicates its distance.

spring—a natural source of water which usually bubbles up from beneath the ground.

succulent—a name given to a group of juicy cacti.

thunderhead—a rounded mass of cumulus cloud, stretching high into the sky, which carries a thunderstorm.

tunnel—any passage or avenue beneath the desert surface made by animals or natural forces.

vulcanism—any of the various manifestations of volcanic activity.

waterhole—a low area where rainwater has accumulated, or a spring or seep.

westerlies—in the United States, winds blowing eastward from the Pacific.

INDEX